D0340334

So Many Kinds of Love

So Many Kinds of Love

By Dean Walley

Illustrated by Barbara White

HALLMARK EDITIONS

So Many Kinds of Love

Life holds so many kinds of love.

Perhaps you have already
discovered every one.
If you haven't,
you will very soon.

When your mother
     tucks you in at night,
     a special kind of love
     fills your heart.

A father gives you a strong,
   secure kind of love.
He may not tell you
   he loves you,
but he doesn't need to.
You just know.

Friendship is another kind of love.
It's a happy feeling you get
when you are laughing
or sharing a secret.

And when you spend
quiet moments together
you know that love
is there, too.

Love isn't always
    just for people.
When a puppy
    follows you everywhere,
    it's his way
    of showing affection.

Kittens show a warm
and trusting kind of love
when they're very drowsy
and go to sleep in your arms.

Even goldfish need love...
especially on rainy days.

Sometimes very simple things
    can mean the world to you --
    like an ice-cold drink of water
    on a hot summer day...

or a warm feather-bed
on a snowy winter night.

Someday, a very special kind of love
    will call you to someone
    who will mean more to you
    than anyone else in the world.

Then you will be very glad
there are so many kinds of love...
and that you have known them all.